Play Piano with...
Elton John

Published by
Wise Publications
14-15 Berners Street, London W1T 3LJ, UK.

Exclusive Distributors:
Music Sales Limited
Distribution Centre, Newmarket Road,
Bury St Edmunds, Suffolk IP33 3YB, UK.
Music Sales Pty Limited
20 Resolution Drive, Caringbah,
NSW 2229, Australia.

Order No. AM955526
ISBN 0-7119-8199-X
This book © Copyright 2000 by Wise Publications.

Compiled by Nick Crispin.
Music arranged by Paul Honey.
Music processed by Enigma Music Production Services.
Cover photograph courtesy of LFI.
Printed in Great Britain by Printwise (Haverhill) Limited, Haverhill, Suffolk.

Your Guarantee of Quality
As publishers, we strive to produce every book to the highest commercial standards.
The music has been freshly engraved and the book has been carefully designed to
minimise awkward page turns and to make playing from it a real pleasure.
Particular care has been given to specifying acid-free, neutral-sized paper made from
pulps which have not been elemental chlorine bleached.
This pulp is from farmed sustainable forests and was produced with special regard for the environment.
Throughout, the printing and binding have been planned to ensure a sturdy,
attractive publication which should give years of enjoyment.
If your copy fails to meet our high standards, please inform us and we will gladly replace it.

www.musicsales.com

Can You Feel The Love Tonight
(From Walt Disney Pictures' "The Lion King")

Words by Tim Rice. Music by Elton John

Gently

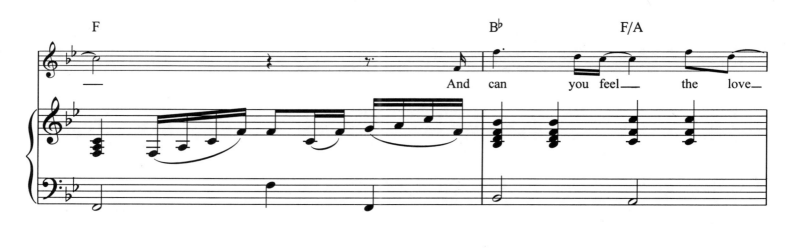

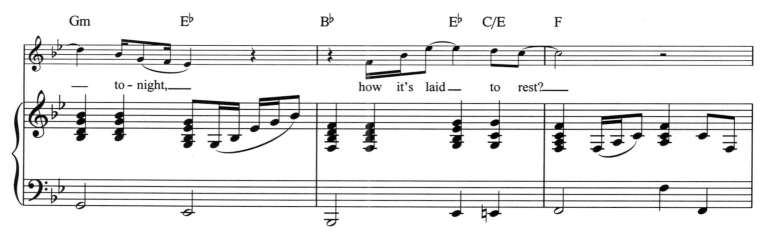

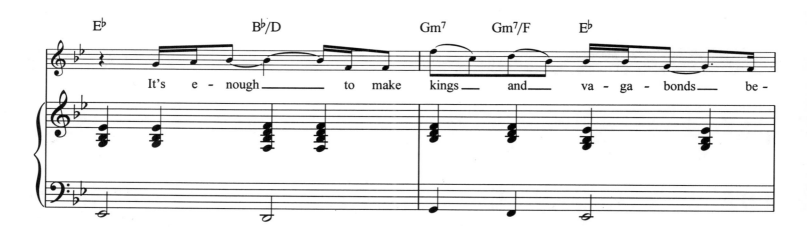

To ⊕ Coda

There's a time for ev-'ry one, if they on-ly learn that the twist-ing ka-lei-do-scope moves us all in turn.

There's a rhyme and rea-son to the wild out-doors

D. % al Coda

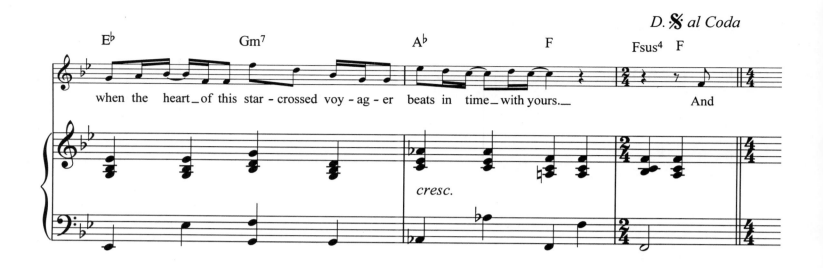

when the heart_ of this star - crossed voy - ag - er beats in time_ with yours._ And

⊕ CODA

It's e - nough_____ to make kings_ and_ va - ga - bonds_ be -

molto rit.

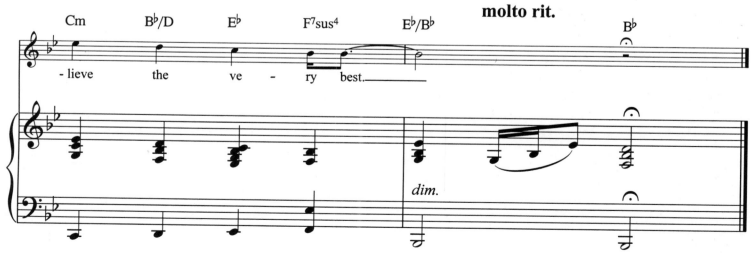

- lieve the ve - ry best._____

Candle In The Wind

Words & Music by Elton John & Bernie Taupin

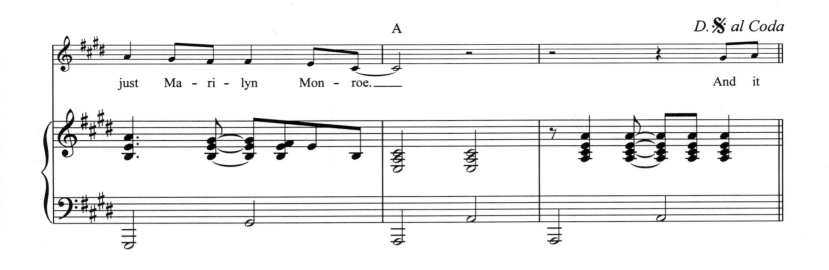

just Ma - ri - lyn Mon - roe.____ And it

CODA

Your can - dle had burned ____ out long ____ be - fore ____ your

leg - end ev - er did.____

Goodbye Yellow Brick Road

Words & Music by Elton John & Bernie Taupin

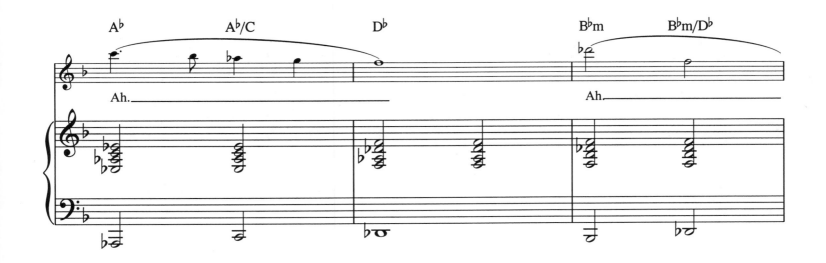

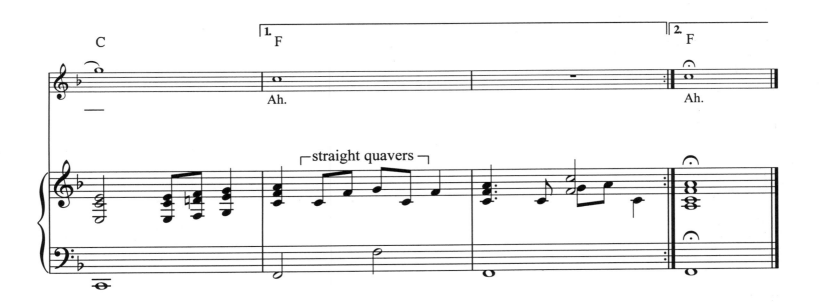

Verse 2:
What do you think you'll do then?
I bet that'll shoot down your plane.
It'll take you a couple of vodka and tonics
To set you on your feet again.
Maybe you'll get a replacement,
There's plenty like me to be found.
Mongrels who ain't got a penny
Singing for titbits like you on the ground.
Ah, ah.

So goodbye yellow brick road, *etc*.

I Guess That's Why They Call It The Blues

Words & Music by Elton John, Bernie Taupin & Davey Johnstone

Verse 2:
Just stare into space
Picture my face in your hands.
Live for each second without hesitation,
And never forget I'm your man.
Wait on me girl,
Cry in the night if it helps.
But more than ever, I simply love you,
More than I love life itself.

And I guess *etc.*

Song For Guy

Words & Music by Elton John

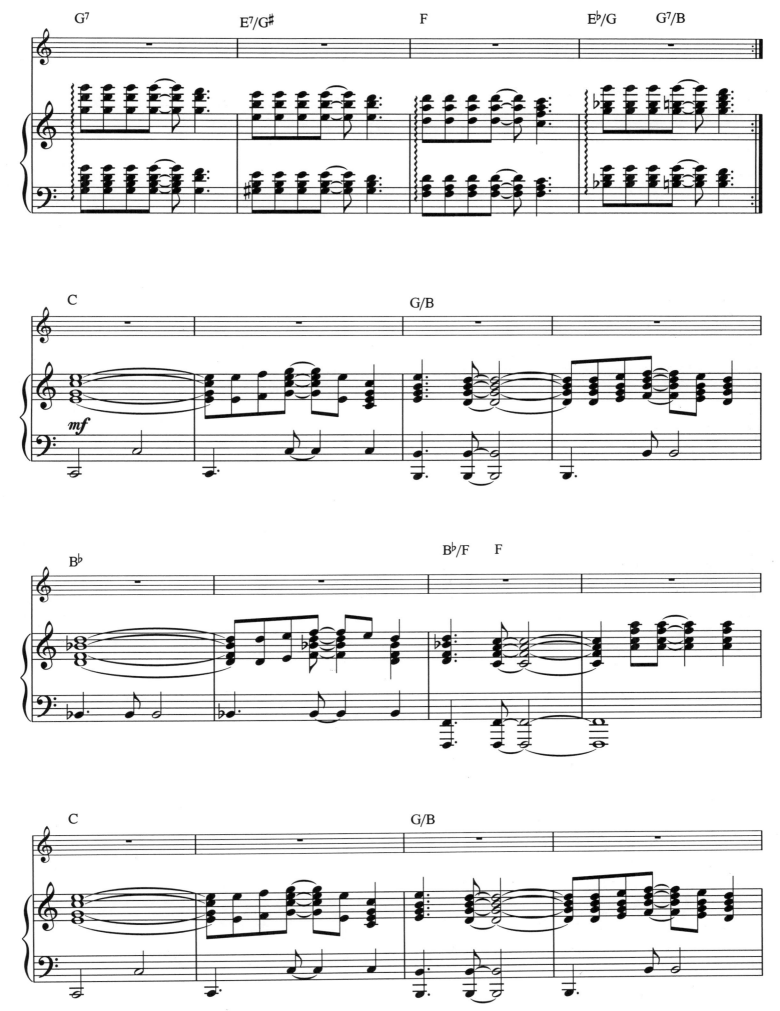

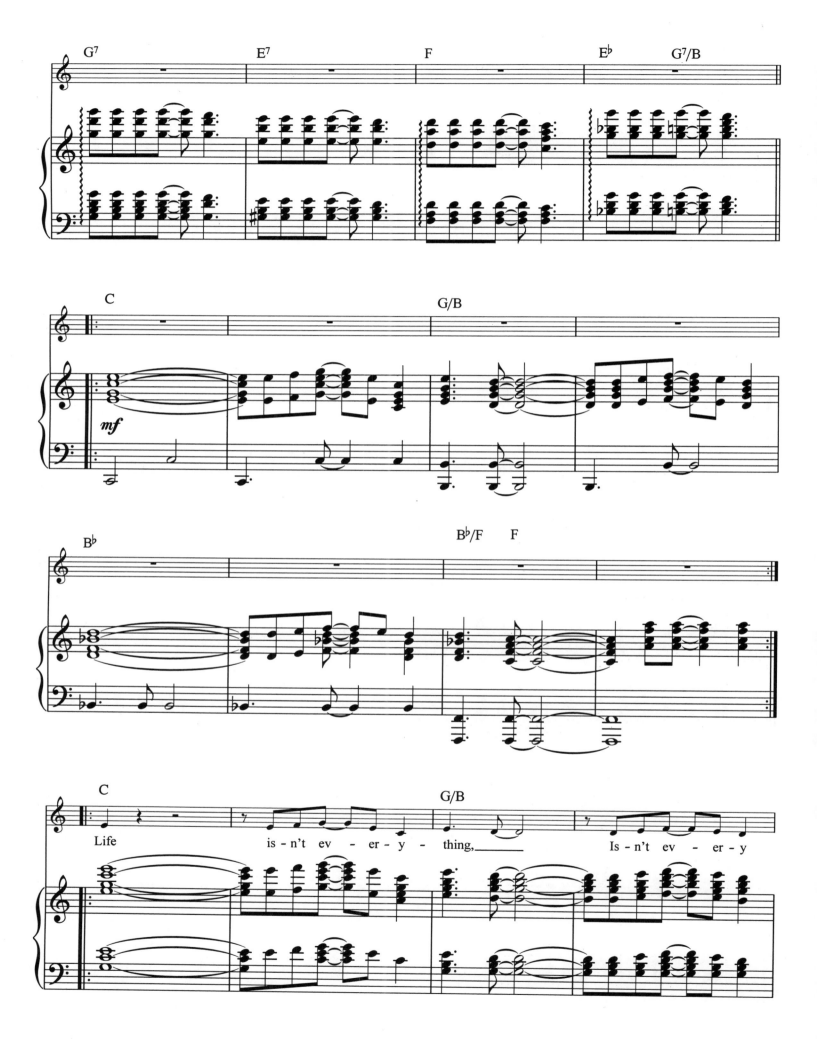

Life is-n't ev - er - y - thing,_____ Is-n't ev - er - y

34

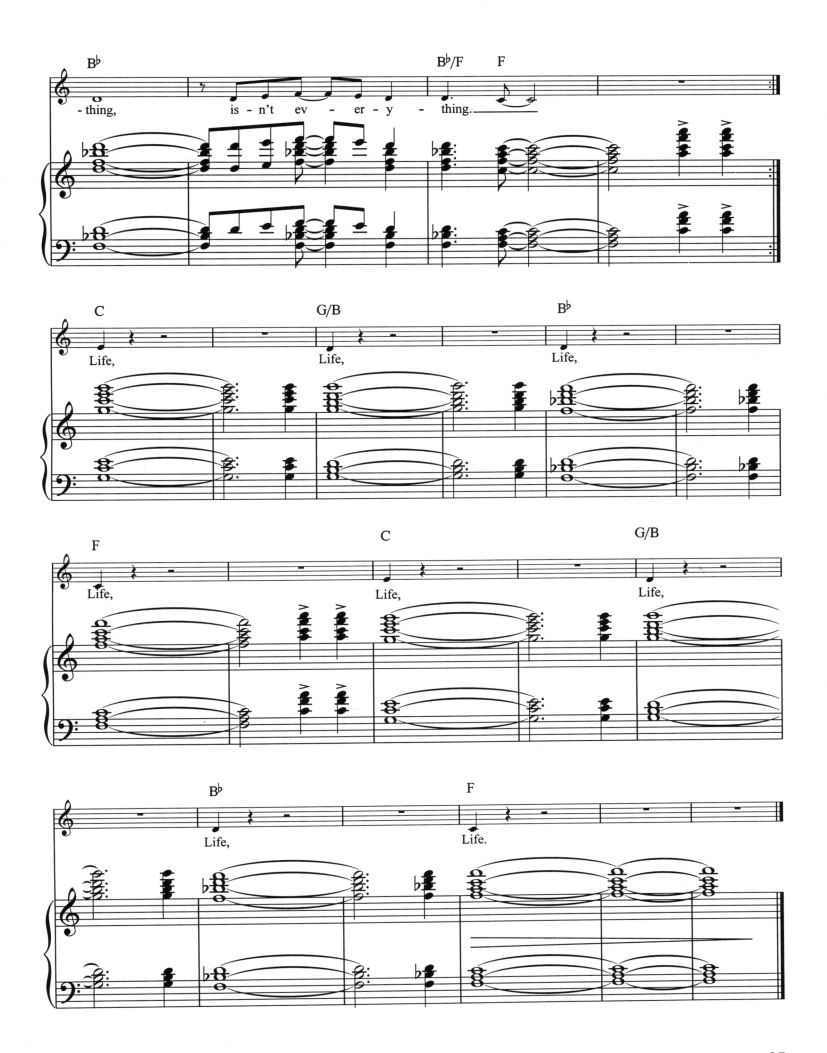

Your Song

Words & Music by Elton John & Bernie Taupin

Flowing

2 bar count in:

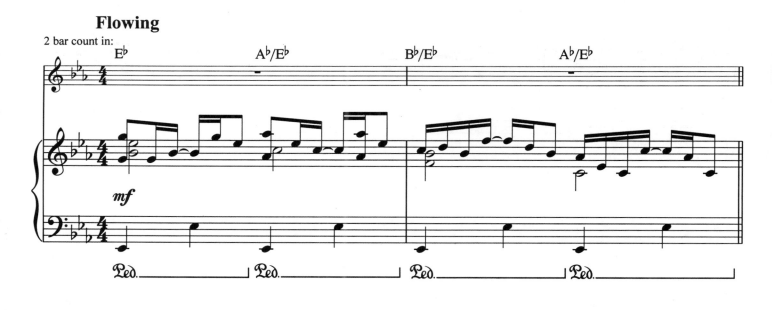

1. It's a lit-tle bit fun-ny___ this feel-ing in - side.___
(Verse 3 see block lyric)

I'm not one of those___ who__ can ea - si - ly hide,___

It may — be quite — sim-ple but, now that it's done,

I hope you don't mind, — I hope you don't mind — that I put down in — words —

— how won-der-ful life is — while you're in — the world. —

D. 𝄋 al Coda

⊕ CODA

I hope you don't mind, ___ I hope you don't mind ___ that I put ___ down in ___ words ___

how won - der - ful life is ___ while you're ___ in ___ the world. ___

I hope you don't mind, ___ I hope you don't mind ___

that I put ___ down in ___ words ___ how won - der - ful life is ___ while

poco rit.

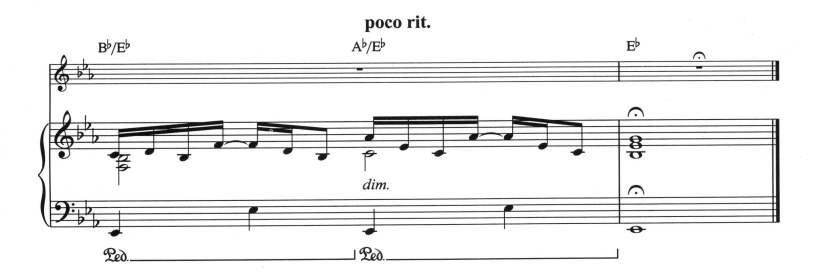

dim.

Verse 3:
I sat on the roof and kicked off the moss,
Well a few of the verses, well they've got me quite cross.
But the sun's been quite kind while I wrote this song,
It's for people like you, that keep it turned on.

Verse 4:
So excuse me forgetting but these things I do,
You see, I've forgotten if they're green or they're blue,
Anyway the thing is what I really mean,
Yours are the sweetest eyes I've ever seen.

And you can tell everybody, *etc.*

Rocket Man

Words & Music by Elton John & Bernie Taupin

And all this sci-ence I don't un-der-stand.

it's just my job five days a week. A rock-et

man, a rock-et man.

And I think it's gon-na be a long,_ long time_ till touch-down brings_ me 'round a-gain to find_ I'm not the man_ they think I am at home,_ oh no,_ no, no,_ I'm a rock-et man._ Rock-et man_ burn - ing out his fuse up here_

10/09 (171824)